D1317866

Crossroads of Conquerors

CROSSROADS
OF
CONQUERORS
The West Indies

by F. Wenderoth Saunders

Illustrated by the Author

Boston Little, Brown and Company Toronto

Published simultaneously in Canada
by Little, Brown & Company (Canada) Limited

PRINTED IN THE UNITED STATES OF AMERICA

Contents

FLORIDA

NASSAU

BAHAMA ISLANDS

CUBA

ISLE OF PINES

TORTUGA

DOMINICAN REPUBLIC

CAYMANS

PUERTO RI

NAVASSA

HAITI

VIRGIN IS.

JAMAICA

SABA
ANTIG
ST. KITTS
NEVIS
MONTSERRA

GUADELOUPE

DOMINICA

MARTINIQUE

CARIBBEAN   SEA

SANTA LUCIA
BARBAD
ST. VINCENT

BONAIRE
CURAÇAO
ARUBA

MARGARITA

GRENADINES

GRENADA

TOBAGO

SAN BLAS IS.

TRINIDA

The West Indies

The Bahamas

THE several thousand islands and islets of the Bahamas look on the map as if someone had seized a full paintbrush and spattered a long arc southeastward from Florida. One of these spatterings, no one is sure which, is the first land Columbus saw in the New World. Since his time a pageant of Spanish knights, pirates, wreckers, colonists, refugees, blockade runners, rumrunners, and tourists has paraded in and out of the Bahamas.

1

Except for the lowness of the land the Bahamas are a preview of the entire West Indies. The predominating race is Negro. Negroes were brought as slaves to replace the Indians, whom the Spaniards took away to cultivate the more fertile lands of Cuba. The Negroes live about as they do in two other British islands, Jamaica and Barbados.

The Bahamas have the whitest beaches, the bluest waters, turning jade-green in the shallows, and rocks of vivid purple under water. The Gulf Stream keeps the islands warm, as warm as many islands farther to the south. And the trade wind blows the long fringes of graceful coconut palms.

The British have ruled the Bahamas most of the time since the reign of Charles I. After our Revolutionary War large numbers of families still loyal to England left Georgia and the Carolinas and began life again in the Bahamas, especially in Nassau. One island, Green Turtle Cay, is populated almost entirely by the descendants of Loyalists who came from the American colonies. The settlement still looks like an American fishing village of a hundred and fifty years ago.

The Andros group, largest of all, is shaped like a giant foot. It is one vast jungle, with places on it people have never reached. Another island, Maya-guana, looks like a slice from the uncivilized part of the Congo. Harbour Island, near the much larger Eleuthera, has fine winter homes belonging to rich Americans and British.

The Bahamas, lying across the trade route from the east coast of North America to Cuba and to the south, were favorite hiding places for pirates. Blackbeard and Captain Kidd popped in and out of the islands to strike terror to merchant shipping. Right in the middle of Nassau stood a gigantic fig tree under which Blackbeard used to hold his councils and from which he hanged his prisoners.

People used to make their living in various curious ways in the Bahamas: some as "wreckers," by hanging lanterns in trees to lure ships onto rocks in order to loot them. Other Bahamans made fortunes during the Civil War in the United States by running English goods past the blockading Union Navy to the hard-pressed Southern states. Still other people, many years later when it was against the law to sell alcoholic drinks in the United States, ran the forbidden liquor into Florida and other places. Now the chief business of the Bahamas is tourists, and the raising of fruits and vegetables is a side line.

Today most visitors go to the twenty-one-mile-long island of New Providence. On it is Nassau, capital of the Bahamas. Nassau has a few old buildings, an old fort or two, markets, shops, many hotels and, besides taxis, some horse-drawn carriages.

Harbour Island

The Capitol, Havana

Cuba

CUBA, the largest island of the West Indies, is shaped like a giant alligator seven hundred and fifty miles long and one hundred and seventy-five miles wide at the belly. It is one of the closest neighbors of the United States. From Cuba some of the greatest Spanish conquerors set forth: Cortez to Mexico, Ponce de León to Florida, and de Soto to the mighty Mississippi.

Cuba is four times larger than Belgium. It has over five million people, or about as many as live in Denmark. The two ends of Cuba are mountainous, while the middle part is mostly rolling plain, covered much of the year with a rippling green sea of sugar cane. For a long, long time Cuba has produced more sugar than any other country in the world.

Most people visiting Cuba fly to the capital, Havana. La Habana, as the Cubans call it, is fascinating. It is the largest city in the West Indies and one of the great seaports of the Western Hemisphere.

4

There are really three Havanas today. The old Spanish city has streets so narrow that trolley-car motormen in turning a corner used to reach out the front window with a long iron hook and pull up the wire fender to keep it from striking the wall of a house. The Plaza de Armas still has several old Spanish government buildings whose deep arches cast black shade from the brilliant sun. The great brassbound wooden doors of these buildings open into cool garden patios.

In Cathedral Square are several old palaces which once belonged to Spanish noblemen. Cubans like to think that Columbus is buried in the cathedral. The niche where his bones were supposed to be is now empty. Either the Spanish took the remains with them when they left Cuba in 1899, or he was never buried in Cuba at all but still lies in the old city of Santo Domingo, capital of the Dominican Republic. Possibly the body that was brought to Havana for burial was that of Christopher Columbus's son Diego.

As you stand in the square and look toward the cathedral, it is easy to imagine the old days when slaves were paraded on the front porch of the church and sold at auction to the highest bidder. The harbor is only a short city block away, and slave ships could tie up to the stone wharf and unload their human cargo.

Negro slaves were in great demand to run the giant sugar plantations. When the Spaniards first settled Cuba, they tried to enslave the Indians, but the Indians died rather than submit to slavery. Only a trace of Indian is left in Cuba—in the province of Pinar del Rio. The Spaniards brought in so many Negroes that they form a big percentage of the population. When you wander about the narrow streets of old Havana, a host of shoeshine boys want to polish your shoes. Men with pushcarts piled high with golden oranges ask you to buy. Or at the corner a Chinese with a glass case mounted on a stand is selling luscious halves of white, fresh-trimmed pineapple, resting on a cake of ice. With the hot morning sun beating down, nothing tastes quite so good as a piece of chilled pineapple.

The ice-cream man, pushing his little cart, tempts you with strange flavors made from tropical fruits. The lollipop vendor carries his candies in a many-storied rack, covered with mosquito netting to keep off the flies. From door to door the dry-goods merchant staggers under a mountain of brightly colored cloth, carried on a pole. And from a distance comes the cry of the hot-tamale vendor selling bits of roast pork buried in layers of corn meal mush flavored with hot peppers, the whole wrapped in corn husks and so near the boiling point that it scalds your tongue.

The most famous of all vendors is El Manisero, the Peanut Vendor. Immortalized in a song by the same name, he carries his little bags of fresh-roasted peanuts in a square tin slung over one shoulder. Vendors, along with laborers, wear cotton trousers, shirts whose tails are left out for coolness, wide-brimmed straw hats, and canvas shoes with coiled-rope soles.

Perhaps you will stop at a coffee shop, not more than a hole in the wall, and watch the waiter shovel a great mound of sugar into your glass, pour some thick black-roasted coffee syrup on top of it, and then fill the glass with hot milk. *Café con leche* (coffee with milk) the Cubans call it. They drink coffee this way or in small cups, black, at all times of the day or evening.

The plan of the older houses, which are built around an open courtyard, or patio, with a fountain playing in the middle, is called Mediterranean. The ancient Greeks and Romans and later the Moors in Spain used the design. The Moors learned that water cast up by a fountain jet cools the air.

In the Plaza de Armas (where Spanish soldiers used to drill) there is a little building called El Templete (the Little Temple). It looks something like a tiny Greek temple. Enclosing it is a high fence supported by six stone pillars, each with a carved pineapple on top. Inside the fence, along with the temple, is a ceiba tree and a statue of Columbus. Every year on St. Christopher's Day hundreds of people line up, to walk around the ceiba tree six times and thus bring themselves good luck for the coming year.

On this spot on St. Christopher's Day, November 16, 1519 (a hundred and one years before the Pilgrims landed at Plymouth, Massachusetts), Havana officially became a city. The stone pineapples represent the fruit presented by the Indians to the Spaniards as a sign of hospitality. The original inhabitants considered the pineapple their best fruit.

A Cuban boy (or girl) does not have a party on his real birthday but has one on the day of celebration for the saint after whom he is named. Thus if a boy's name is Francisco, his party will be on the day of celebration for Saint Francis. In all Spanish-speaking countries this custom is followed.

As Havana grew larger, it overflowed the walls of the old Spanish city and crossed the Prado, the former parade ground, westward into the Vedado. This was once a section of fine old houses whose red tile roofs shone in tropical gardens filled with palm trees, bougainvillaea and jasmine. But a modern invasion of many-storied apartment houses, hotels and office buildings has robbed the Vedado of part of its charm. Here on the waterfront is the beautiful drive called the Malecón, protected by a curving sea wall.

The
Lollipop
Man

The third Havana begins across the Almendares River, a district of modern homes that looks more like Florida and California than the West Indies. Cubans flock to enjoy its beaches, the yacht club and horse racing.

Havana, like any big city, has surrounding suburbs where people live and from which they come to the downtown part of the city to work. The newer suburbs are built along the seashore west of the city because people like to look at the water and it is cooler there. Older Spanish towns, Regla, Guanabacoa, and Casa Blanca, cluster around the harbor.

From Havana you can cross over to Casa Blanca (White House) by ferryboat, but it is more fun to be rowed over in a bumboat for a few pennies. Familiar sights on the hilly, up-and-down streets are charcoal carts shaped like small covered wagons, men riding horseback, balancing tins of water from the public fountain, and fishermen with mended nets on the way to their boats.

Almost above Casa Blanca rises the great pink Cabaña Fortress, and beyond it on the very end of a headland, Morro Castle, which used to protect the harbor entrance. The Spaniards chose the site of Havana because it has a fine natural harbor that must be entered by a fairly wide but long and deep channel.

Havana was not the first Spanish city to be built in Cuba. Columbus landed near the eastern end of the island and some cities there are older. Spain tried to keep all other countries out of the West Indies, but when galleonloads of gold and silver began to come from conquered Peru and Mexico, pirates from many nations swarmed in like flies to honey.

After Havana had been looted and burned twice by French pirates, the Spanish built three forts: La Punta, La Fuerza, and finally the formidable Morro Castle. Havana seemed so impregnable that the great plate fleets refitted there before completing the journey to Spain. Even so, one silver fleet from Mexico was ambushed, after a fake attack on Havana, by two Dutch captains with an armada of thirty ships. Their booty was tremendous. Then for one hundred and twenty-five years Havana and Cuba were safe behind the strong forts.

A few years before the American Revolution, lightning struck. After capturing Quebec and annexing Canada in the French and Indian War, England determined to punish Spain for siding with France. The rich island of Cuba was the target.

The English leader, Lord Albemarle, knew that he could not force the heavily defended channel so he landed his army, which contained several New England regiments, on the headland to the rear of Morro Castle. The Spaniards defended the fortress heroically for fifteen days, but Albemarle conquered and turned the castle's cannon on Havana. The great port surrendered in a hurry! The English ruled the city for a year and opened the port to free trade.

When Spain got Havana back, the government built the huge Cabaña Fortress to protect Morro's blind side. But the seeds that were to flower into independence a century later no walls could keep out. Havana's merchants had so profited by free trade that they continually fought against the old trade restrictions imposed by Spain.

Walls and guns are powerless against another enemy—the hurricane. From time to time the West Indies have been blasted by these frightful windstorms. The hurricane season lasts from about the middle of August through October. Great masses of hot air gather out in the Caribbean Sea or the Atlantic Ocean and begin to swirl upward and round and round at speeds sometimes faster than a hundred miles an hour. Then the entire whirling mass begins to move forward slowly. The slow speed keeps the great revolving air mass over one spot for a long time, and it can do a frightful amount of damage to life and property before it moves on.

Country huts are blown to bits. Even walls of stone buildings are tumbled down when winds are trapped inside. Trees fall like ten pins by the hundreds. Signs and metal roofs hurtle through the air with murderous force. Torrents of rain fall, flooding the streets and the first floors of houses. Fishing ships are blown over and sunk; anyone foolish enough to stay on board is drowned. The storm makes a tangled mess of power and telephone lines, and at the end of the great blow, which sometimes lasts as long as twelve hours, even a great city like Havana looks as though a human enemy had attacked it for many days.

South of Havana on the Caribbean Sea, where Cuba is only thirty-five
miles wide, is a fascinating little seaport called Batabano. From this harbor
fishermen go out after sponges. The sponge is a primitive animal who can't
move about because he is anchored to the bottom of the sea. He takes in
food from the sea water passing through his pores. The part of the sponge
that is used in cleaning bathtubs or washing cars is his skeleton, which is
quite soft when it is soaked in water.

Fourteen men are needed to man a sponge vessel, which does two kinds
of fishing. In water no deeper than thirty feet, men called hookers put out
in rowboats from the mother craft. They peer down through glass-bottomed
buckets and after locating a sponge they rake it in with a three-pronged
hook. In deeper water, up to one hundred and fifty feet, divers go down to
bring up sponges.

Some distance south of Batabano is Cuba's most famous island, the Isle of Pines. Perhaps Robert Louis Stevenson had the Isle of Pines in mind when he wrote *Treasure Island*. Its peculiar shape and its hills and swamps are similar to those Stevenson described, but the only gold to be found there is in its oranges and grapefruit. There is so much marble that buildings and even roads are made of marble rather than concrete.

In the western state of Pinar del Rio, named for its rare pine trees, the mountains are not very high but they are peculiar. The Cubans call them *mogotes*, or sponge mountains. The mogotes rise up directly from the level plain, where the Cubans farm.

The Cuban farmer is called a *guajiro*. The hut he lives in is a *bohio*. The bohio was originally an Indian hut, and has changed little since the days of Columbus. It can be found almost everywhere in the country districts of the West Indies.

When a guajiro wants to build a house, his neighbors help him. They make the frame out of poles tied together with thick tough liana vines. The vines shrink as they dry, and hold the framework in a tight grip. The guajiros weave long pieces of palm bark in and out of the poles to make the sides,

nar del Rio

unless the owner has money to buy rough boards. Thick bundles of palm leaves are tied together to thatch the roof. The floor of the bohio is hard-packed earth, and pigs and chickens wander in and out of the house at will.

The high-peaked roof and the thick insulation of the palm-leaf thatch keep the house quite cool and airy. If you look into a bohio during the day, you wonder where the people sleep. At night they take out hammocks and hang them in the corners.

Pork is the Cubans' favorite meat. Many of the guajiros in Pinar del Rio keep small herds of swine running half wild in the mountains behind their bohios. The many palms of the mogote jungles furnish a rich supply of seeds, or mast, which the pigs love.

To make sure that his pigs do not go completely wild and thus be lost to him, once a week at least the guajiro rides out on his tough mountain pony to find his herd, a bag of grain tied to his saddlebow. When he nears a certain spot, the same every week, he gives a strange call that echoes through the trees to the farthest end of the valley. Presently there is a crashing in the jungle, and then near at hand the inquiring grunts of a small army of pigs, long-legged and rangy. Scattering the corn kernels in handfuls, the guajiro empties his bag.

If he wants a Sunday feast for his family, the guajiro will jump from his horse, snare a young pig, dump him squealing into a bag, remount his horse before the old boar can attack him, and gallop away.

Cuban
Traveling
Restaurant

Roast young pig cooked Cuban country style is the most delicious of meat dishes. I first tasted it cooked by a guajiro named Domingo who was serving as a mountain guide. He built a big fire out of bits of dried wood. While the fire was burning itself into a mass of hot coals, Domingo split open the pig and cracked the joints, working wild lime juice into the openings. Then, after flattening the two halves of the pig, he laid it on a cradle of green twigs, suspended over the glowing mass of coals. Using his long knife, called a machete, Domingo quickly sliced down a number of palm leaves until he had enough to cover the cooking pig completely. For two hours and a half the pig baked in its palm oven while we rode off to explore a mountain valley, take a swim in a pool, and return finally to the feast.

For Christmas dinner, which comes very early in the morning after midnight mass on Christmas Eve, roast pig is the national dish. In the cities, on the morning of the day before Christmas, boys or servants carry whole young pigs, prepared on flat pans, to bakeries where they are cooked, and bring them home again just before the evening church service.

Some of the guajiros in Pinar del Rio are part Indian and they are very clever at spearing fish in mountain pools. If possible they work in pairs. One guajiro will jump into one end of the pool and splash noisily around until he frightens fish to the other end, where his companion waits motionless with his slender spear poised. Spearing fish requires much skill and practice, for when you are standing above the water and looking down into it, the spear appears to bend where it enters the water.

After sugar, tobacco is of next importance as a farm crop. The best in the world is grown in a section of Pinar del Rio called Vuelta Abajo, or The Land That Turns Down from Havana. Europeans knew nothing about tobacco until Columbus and his men saw Indians with strange smoking machines fitted into their nostrils. After Columbus's return, smoking became popular in Europe, and the Spaniards soon made a lot of money from tobacco.

Some of the very best cigars are still made by hand in Havana. The cigar makers twist or roll the insides, called fillers, and around them bend fine smooth leaves that have had the coarse veins removed. While the cigar makers work, a man or woman reads aloud to them all day long: stories, news and sporting news.

To go eastward from Havana one can take an electric line at Casa Blanca for Matanzas. On the way the cars pass through the town of Hershey, where a sugar mill is located and from which the sugar for candy bars has come. Beyond Hershey the train passes through beautiful Yumuri Valley with its fruit orchards and its bright green fields of sugar cane, the whole crisscrossed with rows of royal palms.

Cuba is a perfect place to grow sugar. Since the island is just inside the torrid zone, there are no frosts to kill the thick juicy cane stalks, which need nearly nine months to grow. The bright red soil of the island is so rich that even the fence posts take root. If you cut down a small tree, make a fence post out of part of the trunk, and stick it into the ground, it will start to sprout.

ing Sugar Cane

When the cane is ripe, guajiros swarm into the fields with their machetes to cut down the stalks, now growing taller than a man. The cut cane is piled into high two-wheeled oxcarts, or into trucks, or if the central (sugar factory) is a long way from the fields, into little narrow-gauge railway cars. At the central the cane is ground, the juices are boiled off for molasses, rum, and industrial alcohol, and the coarse grains left in the vats are shipped to refineries in other countries to be ground into sugar.

The electric line ends at Matanzas, a city with one of the best harbors in the Western Hemisphere, an old city with wide streets and Spanish colonial buildings, a city famous for its poets and writers, a city called the Athens of Cuba. Like Athens it has a high part from which one can see the Yumuri Valley and the beautiful landlocked bay. In the newer part of the city are factories, and part way round the bay are the famous Bellamar Caves.

Geologists say all of Cuba is honeycombed with caves cut by dripping water and underground rivers, but the Bellamar Caves are famous as an underground fairyland. A Chinese slave discovered them by accident in 1862. He was digging out rock for a wall. Suddenly the ground opened up at his feet. The slave was so surprised he dropped his crowbar down the hole and rushed back to his master with the news. When he went back to recover the tool, he found the caves.

Well over a hundred feet below ground, the now lighted caves are a whole series of connected caverns a mile long. The colored rock formations of stalactites and stalagmites take hundreds of strange shapes. There is a saying that if you want to get married, you should drink from a special pool in the caves.

An Old Kitchen   Charcoal Stoves

Spanish Bridge
Sancti Spiritus

East of Matanzas are a number of more modern cities. Cárdenas has a dazzling white sand beach called Varadero, which is well known to American tourists. Santa Clara is a business city, as is Cienfuegos, which was settled first by French colonists from Louisiana. At Cienfuegos, Cubans and Americans have made one of the world's most important botanical gardens, complete with sausage trees, fifty classes of sugar cane, and a thousand varieties of palms.

At Sancti Spíritus and Trinidad, you can see how people lived one hundred and two hundred years ago. Both old towns have fine ancient buildings that look as though they might have come direct from Southern Spain. Trinidad is so old that people can point to a spot just below town where they think Cortez tied the flagship of his fleet to a tree. Once Trinidad was so wealthy from raising sugar with slave labor that any time pirates were short of gold they raided the town. A number of rich plantation owners built large and splendid palaces there.

While Cuba belonged to Spain, the Spanish governors went to Trinidad to spend the summer and to be entertained. Slaves laid the crooked, cobblestone streets. Palaces built of Italian marble, coral rock, and Cuban mahoganies and decorated with French tapestries were each as large as a city block.

The builder of the most fabulous palace was not a Spaniard or even a Cuban but a Yankee shipmaster and trader named Baker, from Philadelphia. Like King Midas, he found that almost everything he touched turned to gold. Baker made most of his money trading in sugar. He married a Cuban lady, and settled down in Trinidad. He gave a Spanish spelling to his name, Béquer, but this left the pronunciation unchanged.

19

Unfortunately the Béquer Palace was torn down a long time ago, but people still talk about it, especially the second floor where the family lived. (In these palaces the downstairs was for the kitchen, the laundry and the servants.) Béquer paved his salon—the great parlor where he received guests—with gold coins. The Spanish governor, however, made such a fuss about the disrespect of people's walking on the face of the Spanish king, whose phiz was on the gold coins, that Béquer had them taken up and put on edge.

Even though the Béquer palace is gone, there are enough other palaces, old churches and towers remaining to give a good idea of what Cuba looked like in times past. Because the island is warm most of the year, the ceilings of the palaces are high and the floors are covered with cool tiles; there was no air conditioning then.

Most young people would enjoy the Trinidad desserts, because they are absolutely the sweetest in the world, but I wonder how they would like the Trinidad custom of "going steady." It is called "plucking the turkey." After a young man has permission to call on a young lady, he can only do so in a very special way. The young lady stands or sits in an open window on the ground floor, and the young man takes his place in the street directly before her. A grille of iron or wood stands between them. *And* they are in full view of all the people passing by on the street.

Trinidad

Cuba has several other cities of interest. Camagüey, the third largest city on the island, rapidly growing and modernized, with many factories and an international airport, is in the leading sugar, cattle, pineapple, and citrus-fruit region. East of Camagüey are two cities famous in Cuba's struggle for independence from the Spaniards, Bayamo and Santiago de Cuba.

Among the many great patriots who have struggled desperately to make Cuba free, three men stand out above all others. Statues to them are to be found all over the island. José Martí, the symbol of Cuban freedom, was a poet and a man of gifted speech who had the power to inspire men to give their wealth and their lives for Cuba. Máximo Gómez y Báez, skilled in bush fighting, became supreme army commander in the war begun in 1895. Antonio Maceo was a fearless, dashing cavalry leader whose hit-and-run battles kept the Spaniards guessing.

The war began in disaster for the Cubans: both Maceo and Martí were killed. But the Cubans rallied behind General Gómez. The Spaniards could not capture this great Cuban general. The Spaniards held the cities, but the Cubans held the countryside.

To protect American interests and rights, the United States sent the battleship *Maine* to Havana. While there, the *Maine* blew up from an unknown cause, but many Americans thought that the Spaniards had caused the explosion. Shouting "Remember the Maine!" those who wanted to liberate Cuba were strong enough to lead the United States to declare war on Spain.

Immediately the United States sent Lieutenant Andrew Somers Rowan with the famous "message to Garcia," to tell the Cubans that American help was coming. Lieutenant Rowan went to Jamaica and from there landed on the east coast of Cuba. Patriots guided him over the Sierra Maestra, the highest mountains on the island. These are the same mountains from which Castro came down to overthrow Batista, the same mountains where anti-Castro forces fought. Rowan's party, battling mosquitoes, sweltering heat, drenching rains, hunger, and danger of capture, won through to Bayamo, where General Calixto Garcia was fighting Spaniards.

When the war with Spain started, the Spanish fleet for safety sailed into the bay of Santiago de Cuba. Santiago is built on hills at the head of a long bay, surrounded by more hills and mountains. Today there are still many old buildings in Santiago, but the most exciting of all the old structures is out-

Entrance to Santiago de Cuba

side the city. It is another Morro Castle, guarding the entrance to the bay. Morro Castle and other batteries kept the American fleet from following the Spanish into the bay.

Unopposed, an American army landed east of Santiago. Among the forces was a famous regiment called the Rough Riders, recruited and commanded by General Leonard Wood and Colonel Theodore (Teddy) Roosevelt. When the Americans, after a desperate struggle, took the two key hills defending Santiago, the Spanish had to surrender. The Spanish fleet tried to fight its way out of the harbor but was wiped out. The war was over and Cuba was free.

For its help, the United States was allowed by Cuba to build the giant naval base on Guantánamo Bay east of Santiago. It is an important training station and defense for the Panama Canal.

Jamaica

WHEN Columbus was asked by his sovereigns to describe some of the larger islands of the West Indies, the Admiral of the Ocean Sea took a sheet of paper, crumpled it in his hands and put it on the table. Seen from the air, Jamaica is like a crumpled piece of bright green paper, with very narrow coastal plains and gleaming white beaches. Its high mountains make it a land of many climates: from tropical heat in the lowlands to occasional sleet on the highest mountaintops.

Dwarf rivers run from the highlands to the sea, carrying off the rainfall, which can flood up to sixteen inches in twenty-four hours in the rainy season. Jamaica is indeed the Arawak Indian Xaymaca—"Isle of Many Rivers." The rivers twist through the hills, tear down the mountainsides, and fling themselves from rocks in lacy waterfalls.

Many visitors see only one spot—Montego Bay on the north coast of Jamaica. They come from the cold north in the winter to lie on the beaches, go sea fishing, and stay in the luxury hotels. But Montego Bay is not Jamaica. Although Columbus landed on the north coast, the place to find Jamaica is in the south. Here are Spanish Town, Kingston, Port Royal, the Blue Mountains, and the past.

Kingston, the capital, has one of the six best landlocked harbors in the world. A long, slender spit of sand, the Palisadoes, is a natural breakwater which encloses the harbor completely except for a narrow entrance. But Kingston was not the first town on this harbor site.

From its earliest days Jamaica was *the* pirate island of the West Indies. So pirates could not attack without warning, the early Spanish settlers built their capital, now called Spanish Town, ten miles back from the coast. For a seaport they used the present Kingston harbor, putting a rough fort of palisades (pointed logs) on the sandspit breakwater.

The English sent several military expeditions against Jamaica and finally conquered it in the middle 1600's. On the breakwater they built forts of stone and a town which they named Port Royal. In a few years Port Royal became the greatest pirate town and the wickedest place in the world. Jamaica was right in the middle of the Spanish king's trade routes between his gold and silver kingdoms in Peru and Mexico on the one hand and his rich West Indian colonies and Spain on the other.

First, all English pirates made Port Royal their headquarters. Then came the French and the Dutch to join them, all hoping to "singe the beard of the King of Spain." Before he was thirty years old, Sir Henry Morgan became the bully of Port Royal. Absolutely without fear, Morgan was fierce as a wildcat and cunning as a fox. Like an admiral of the pirate fleets, he planned and executed the most daring raids in the entire history of the Caribbean.

Loading Sugar Cane

Morgan's greatest feat was to lead a small army of sixteen hundred pirates and soldiers across the Isthmus of Panama through forty-nine miles of fever-ridden jungle. Plagued by heat, insects and hostile Indians, his men put to rout a superior force of Spaniards. When the smoke of battle cleared, old Panama lay burned so badly that the survivors had to rebuild in a new location, where Panama City is today. Morgan's men sifted the ashes and brought back rich booty to Port Royal.

For this exploit, Charles II of England knighted Morgan and returned him to Jamaica as governor with orders to put an end to piracy. Port Royal in Morgan's day was a roistering, boisterous town where private fortunes were gambled away overnight. Merchants came in large numbers to buy up pirate loot at reduced prices, and ship it out again.

One June morning four years after Morgan's death, there was a rumbling in the mountains. Then suddenly the earth was torn apart. The spit of land enclosing the harbor tilted to one side, and two thirds of Port Royal slid into the sea.

With Port Royal vanished some two thousand people. In the spring and summer of 1959 a diving expedition brought to the surface many relics from the sunken city: cannons, cooking utensils, a pot with stew bones still in it, clay smoking pipes, wine bottles, lanterns, even a brass watch that had stopped three minutes after the quake. Evidently it had taken that long for water to get to its works when its owner slid into the sea.

Airplanes now land on the sandspit that connects what is left of Port Royal with the mainland. After the disaster the survivors built a new city on the mainland. They laid out the present port of Kingston as a business town, with its streets in a straight checkerboard pattern. Were it not for its backdrop, Kingston would have little beauty. The backdrop is the Blue Mountains, the second highest ridge in the West Indies, with a peak that is something over seven thousand feet.

Jamaica became a sugar-rich island, its plantations rivaling the great estates of Haiti. Some of the estate houses which survive have been turned into hotels. Rose Hall, near Montego Bay, the most magnificent of all plantation houses, is now only a ruined shell. In this palace of great stairways, mahogany doors, gilt, costly paintings, and resplendent chandeliers, two hundred people at a time sat down in the banquet hall.

On certain nights Jamaicans who live in the vicinity of Rose Hall think they see the White Witch, the ghost of the wife of one of the owners. Supposedly she was trampled to death under a mattress because of her cruel treatment of her slaves.

Another ruin is Colbeck Castle, the largest building ever constructed on Jamaica. Half palace and half fort, it may have protected its owners from Spanish raiders or from the possibility of slave uprisings. Since the white population was small and slaves were imported by the thousands from Africa to work the fields, white masters lived in perpetual fear. They had reason to be afraid, for in the Cockpit Country, the Land-of-Look-Behind-You, lived the Cimarrónes.

The Cockpit Country, in the western end of Jamaica, is a two-hundred-square-mile hodgepodge of cones, funnels and strange formations of rock where a stranger could quickly become hopelessly lost, and a few men could hold off a small army. When Spanish rule ended on Jamaica, the remaining Indians and the Negroes who had been Spanish slaves retreated into this rocky maze. At first they were called by their Spanish name Cimarrónes, but later just Maroons. From time to time their numbers were increased by escaped slaves from the plantations.

The Maroons

The Maroons would make sudden forays on the great estates, burning the cane fields and houses, and massacring the owners. The whites fought several unsuccessful wars against the Maroons. Finally they had to make a treaty with them guaranteeing their independence in return for an end to bloodshed and the shielding of runaway slaves. Some Maroon settlements, like Accompong and Maroon Town, still exist.

Jamaican Negroes are more like those of the United States than others in the West Indies. They have stories that are closely related to the Br'er Fox tales. The slaves told the Anancy stories to their own children and the children of their white masters.

Anancy was a big black spider as cunning as Br'er Fox, not physically strong but to be feared just the same. "How Monkey Manage Anancy" is a typical story. Told in Jamaican Negro dialect, it begins this way:

One day Anancy an him wife sidung under tree a chat, no kno say Monkey eene tree top a lisen. Hear Anancy, "Me wife, a want a likkle fresh!"

Hear him wife! "What kind a fresh?"

"Any meat at all. Ah tell yuh, wha yuh mek we do."

Try reading this aloud; it will be easier to understand.

Jamaica has many fine auto roads and even railroads from which to see the mountains, beaches and plantations. In Spanish days Jamaica was poor, and Spanish Town, ten miles from Kingston, does not compare in architecture and interest with Trinidad, Cuba. Falmouth, on the north coast of Jamaica, is Georgian English (built in the days of Georges I, II, and III of England), but it is England in a tropical setting.

As elsewhere in the West Indies, there came a time when the price of sugar declined. There was more sugar than people in Europe could eat, especially when the colder countries began to make it out of sugar beets. Jamaicans tried raising bananas and banana planters did well until plant diseases and hurricanes badly damaged the trees. Fortunately botanists have since overcome the killing diseases by developing a new type of tree.

The banana tree is really a big plant that grows from ten to thirty feet high and bears one bunch of fruit only. In nine or ten months the stem in the center of the stalk blossoms. When the petals drop off, you can see a cluster of tiny bananas, which point upward as they grow.

Many other things grow in Jamaica, too: oranges, limes, breadfruit, coconuts, most kinds of vegetables, and the sisal plant, whose dried fibers are twisted into twine and rope.

Modern machinery has made sugar pay again. Jamaica, along with two other British West Indian islands, Barbados and Trinidad, ships a great amount of sugar to England.

In 1942 Jamaican farmers were wondering why grass grew so sparsely in certain places. They tried various kinds of grass seed, but none did well. Then someone discovered that the soil was fifty per cent bauxite. This was a great find, for the useful metal aluminum comes from bauxite.

Bauxite has now become an important mining operation in Jamaica. Its deep red deposits run nearly across the middle of the island. Big steam shovels dig from the surface down and load it into earth-moving trucks. These carry the bauxite either to a smelting plant or to the docks for shipment.

In Jamaica it is fun to take a ride on a raft down the Rio Grande. The rafts are made of thick bamboo poles fastened together. Two people can sit in seats near the stern. The poleman stands toward the bow. With a long bamboo pole he guides the raft around jutting rocks, over low waterfalls and by green-clad hills. On the way you may stop for a picnic lunch and go swimming wherever you like in the sparkling water.

The Cayman Islands

IF you like turtle soup, or lobster, or want to dig for buried treasure or maybe find some pieces of eight, Spanish doubloons or Portuguese moidores washed up on the beaches, you should go to the Cayman Islands. Northwest of Jamaica and due south of Cuba, the Caymans are three in number: Grand Cayman, Little Cayman and Cayman Brac, all under British rule.

The islands were settled originally by pirates and marooned sailors. Grand Cayman is one of the very few islands in the West Indies where whites outnumber blacks. Most of the men go off to sea, either as sailors or turtle fishers.

Once there were plenty of turtles on the Caymans, but now the turtle fishers must cross the Caribbean and pay to catch turtles in Nicaraguan waters. The crews bring back the turtles alive, scratch their initials on the shells, and put the reptiles, which weigh up to six hundred pounds, in wire-meshed pits called turtle crawls. Most of the big creatures are shipped to the United States for food.

Grand Cayman is quite flat, but it has some nice beaches and a coral reef that nearly surrounds the island. Coral is a little sea animal that lives inside its own skeleton. Billions and billions of these stony skeletons cemented together make a reef, which is like a ragged wall partly submerged. The Cayman reef has underwater caves, in which can be found the *langouste,* or warm-water lobster. The langouste is caught with a two-pronged stick.

Another denizen of the Cayman coast is the giant conch. His shell makes a wonderful souvenir. Haitians buy the meat as a delicacy.

The Cayman Islanders may be descended from pirates but their chief interest today is going to church. On Christmas Eve, fathers and mothers sprinkle white sand around their white wooden houses so that when their children wake up on Christmas morning and look out their windows, it will seem as if snow has fallen during the night. The very, very white sand comes from a beach near Georgetown, the capital.

Setting a turtle net

Haiti

TO Columbus Hispaniola was "the fairest paradise on earth." Hispaniola, with Haiti in the west and the Dominican Republic in the east, is truly the most beautiful of the larger islands of the West Indies. And Haiti, with its blending of African and French civilizations, is the most fascinating of all countries. Haiti is a Christian country, but it is also a land of African gods, mystery and magic, a land of talking drums.

In Indian the word *haiti* means "highest land." Mountain ridges like gigantic waves sweep over into the Dominican Republic, where their summits are far higher than any peaks in eastern North or South America.

Nestled down in the mountains of Haiti are three valleys: Plan du Nord (Plain of the North), Artibonite (a central plain, needing some irrigation), and Cul de Sac (Dead End Valley, in the south). Farm lands in these valleys once made Haiti the richest of all countries in the West Indies. But Haiti is now so very poor that even a piece of string or an empty can is valuable!

Port-au-Prince, the capital and largest city of Haiti, is at the head of a long bay where the Cul de Sac meets the sea. It is always hot in Port-au-Prince. When you step from a plane, the heat strikes you like a blast from an open furnace. At sea level and facing west, the city is cut off by the mountains from the cooling breezes of the trade winds that blow over all the islands from east to west. Climatically Port-au-Prince has one advantage: usually bad hurricanes roar over it and not through it.

In Port-au-Prince there are modern stores, hotels, a few factories and warehouses and some ultramodern buildings from a world's fair held in 1952. But there are also old stone buildings with arches and ironshod doors shut at night or when revolution threatens, and typical wooden West Indian houses whose second-story balconies stand on stilts. On the outskirts of the city there are even African wattle huts, covered with palm thatch. Most of the houses in town are roofed with sheets of corrugated iron, some of them bright brown with rust.

A car has to go slowly to keep from running into groups of women carrying on their heads baskets piled high with oranges or bananas or plantains (cooking bananas) or vegetables. The women stride by, flashing their white teeth in a smile or singing a song that is happy but not very melodic. Here and there, donkeys carry women riding on saddle baskets that almost hide the little beasts, who trot briskly forward under their enormous burdens.

In the very center of downtown Port-au-Prince is the Iron Market. It really is made of iron—sheet iron. People swarm around it and into it in such numbers that it looks like a huge anthill.

The great market consists of two large sheds, connected by a central section over which rises an iron tower. The tower is someone's idea of what an East Indian tower looks like. There are many East Indian reminders in this West Indian city. Just after much of Port-au-Prince had burned to the ground in 1896, Haitian architects visited a world's fair in Paris featuring East Indian buildings and decided that the style would look well in Haiti.

IRON MARKET

In the Iron Market there are very few display tables, but the women spread what they have to sell on mats or cloths on the floor and wait patiently for buyers to come. Here are vegetables and fruits, eggs and live chickens, and young pigs; also beautifully woven hats and baskets. And there are gourds to drink out of, and remnants of bright cloth at prices that seem cheap, since the Haitian coin, called the gourde, is worth only twenty cents in United States money. But most Haitian people do not have much money. The utensil shop proves this. Cups and cooking pans are made from tin cans and sell for only a few pennies.

In the Iron Market, women are the storekeepers. Where are the men? At home tending the fields, the farm animals and the small children! The wives hold the purse strings. There are too many things for the countrymen to spend money on in Port-au-Prince. Also, some years ago farmers got into the habit of staying away from market centers. This was in the days when a rebel band called the Cacos was fighting against the government. To get recruits for their forces, the Cacos seized countrymen coming to town and turned them into bushfighters.

You won't find any streetcars in Port-au-Prince. You take a taxi instead. For this the charge is small, but you must share the taxi with several others. When you get into the taxi, it is polite to say in French, *"Bon jour, Messieurs et Mesdames!"* and when you leave, *"Au revoir, Messieurs et Mesdames!"*

Much of the heavy transport of goods is on great hand trucks pushed by men. In Haiti hiring manpower is much cheaper than owning a horse or an auto truck—a gallon of gasoline costs almost what a man earns in a day. Automobiles are very expensive in Haiti. When a car finally gives out, every good part of the machine is carefully detached, cleaned and saved. These pieces are sold to an auto-parts store, where each part is hung by a piece of cord from the ceiling. Auto owners in need of repair parts wander around in these stores until they find pieces that fit their cars.

The elegant district of homes and gardens in Port-au-Prince is on the slopes back from the waterfront. Here is the pink and white cathedral whose two tall towers can be seen far out to sea. But even in these surroundings you may hear the sound of distant throbbing, "Ba-r-room, boom, boom, boom! Ba-r-room, boom, boom, boom!"

It is the sound of jungle Africa, the sound of people in the hills talking to each other. The government allows the hill people to talk on their drums only on week ends. Otherwise no one would sleep in Port-au-Prince on workday nights because the drums throb by night as well as by day.

Some people say that the great bay of Port-au-Prince is as beautiful as the Bay of Naples in Italy. The city is at the end of the bay and in the far distance the island of Gonave acts something like a breakwater.

Almost daily over this island in the late afternoon, giant black storm clouds rise to fantastic heights. When the storm breaks, everyone runs for shelter. The storm lasts about an hour and afterwards the air is cooler. The early evening on a Thursday is a good time to visit the long stone and cement dock that rambles all around the waterfront. Thursday seems to be visiting day for Haitian sailing craft. Nine and ten deep, the small boats tie up so closely that a man can hop easily from one to another.

The boats bring fish and vegetables, fruit and stove charcoal into Port-au-Prince. On the larger boats people cook over little charcoal fires in pans called braziers. To protect themselves from the rain they stretch a square of canvas tentlike over the boom. Most of the craft have one sail only.

Back from the waterfront is a great open place called the Champ de Mars (Field of Mars, the Roman god of war). In West Indian Spanish cities this square is generally known as the Plaza de Armas, the drilling place of the soldiers. Facing the Champ de Mars is the President's Palace, an ivory-white building larger than the White House in the United States.

Touching the harbor side of the Champ de Mars is just about the strangest jail in the world. At mealtimes boys bring in nests of covered dishes, one stacked above another, the whole held together by a metal frame. The smell of hot food comes from the dishes. Prisoners in the jail must be fed by their own families. In this way the government saves money. The food law was also passed because beggars used to join work gangs on their way back to prison in order to be fed free.

Columbus named this second largest island of the West Indies la Española, which in time was changed to Hispaniola. The Spaniards tried to enslave the Indians to work their cattle plantations, but the Indians died. In disgust the Spanish quitted the western side and abandoned their cattle.

In the late 1600's the whole Caribbean buzzed with pirates trying to ambush Spanish gold ships. Needing food, pirates landed on Haiti, killed the now wild cattle, and smoked the meat, which they called *boucan*. From that word came another word for pirates—*buccaneers*.

Many of the pirates liked Haiti and settled there. Since most of them were French, they made Haiti into a French colony. To run their plantations, which produced great quantities of sugar, indigo, rice, coffee, and rum, the French brought in thousands of Negroes from Africa. In time fifty thousand whites ruled five hundred thousand Negroes, who by their work made Haiti France's richest possession. With their enormous wealth the whites built beautiful palaces on a natural harbor, naming the city Cap François.

At this time there grew up another class of people, called mulattoes, whose fathers were white but whose mothers were black. The mulattoes were free and could own property. For many years everything went along fine. Then big trouble started!

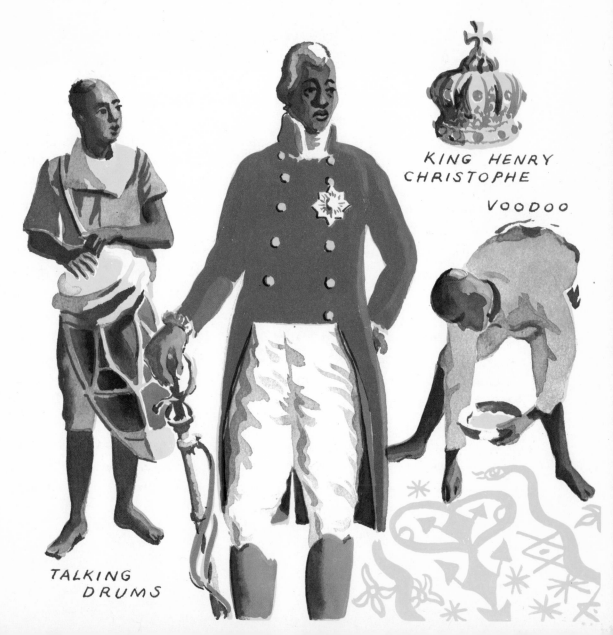

KING HENRY CHRISTOPHE

VOODOO

TALKING DRUMS

The thirteen American Colonies won freedom from England. The new rulers in France, who had killed their king and queen in the French Revolution, said everybody was free. The Haitian slaves thought they ought to be free, too. In the mountains the drums began to talk, and the witch doctors urged the Negroes to revolt. They burned down the houses of some of the cruelest planters, with the planters and their families in them.

A great Negro, Toussaint L'Ouverture, led the revolt. Toussaint drove out the English and the Spaniards who had come to help the French. Many times he defeated an army of fifty thousand French soldiers sent by the great Napoleon. It was in one of these battles that Toussaint got the name L'Ouverture, which means "The Opener," because he opened such a big hole in the enemy's line that they were defeated.

The French general in Haiti was a wily fellow. He pretended to make peace, and tricked Toussaint into a meeting by offering to make him governor over Haiti. When Toussaint came to the meeting with only a few friends, the French general broke his promise, captured Toussaint and shipped him off to France, where he died in prison.

Toussaint's two great generals, Dessalines and Christophe, carried on the war and drove out the French armies. Promising freedom to leave Haiti, Dessalines tricked hundreds of planters and their families into coming to Cap François, where he had his soldiers cut them down with their cane knives. For this he was named "The Butcher."

Jean Jacques Dessalines, former slave, became Emperor Jacques I of Haiti. Hating even the color white, Dessalines ripped the white from the French Tricolor, leaving only the red and blue for the Haitian flag. But Dessalines was cruel even to his own people, so cruel that they assassinated him.

Henry Christophe, the third leader, made himself King Henri I, with his capital at Cap François. This giant of a man, who could bend a horseshoe in his hands, had a dream of greatness for the blacks. He believed that anything the whites could do, the blacks could do just as well or better.

To get money Christophe made his people bring in every gourd that grew. In turn he paid his people in gourds for the things they grew. This made gourds valuable. The name for Haitian money is still gourde, just as we speak of the dollar. Christophe sold Haitian farm products in Europe for gold to buy the things he wanted.

He built a beautiful palace called Sans Souci, which means "without care."

Few palaces are any larger than Sans Souci. Faced with marble from Europe, the palace had pipes under the floors running with cold mountain water to cool the temperature a hundred and twenty years before air conditioning. The palace is now in ruins.

Fearing the French might come back, Christophe built a great fortress on a mountain top. The citadel, named Le Ferrier after the French engineer hired to build it, still defies the jungle. Big enough to hold ten thousand men with supplies for a long siege, the citadel rivals the great pyramids of Egypt. Thousands died dragging the massive stones and cannon to the location. Christophe worked his people harder and harder so he could build roads and schools and hire foreign teachers. He even watched the mountainsides with a powerful telescope, and if he found a man loafing, he had him whipped. Although the people feared him, they began to grumble quietly just the same.

One day Christophe became paralyzed on one side. His fine army deserted him. Most of his friends whom he had made into dukes and counts ran away when they heard the drums in the mountains talking about vengeance. But Christophe was a great showman to the last. Somehow the crippled king shot himself with a silver bullet which he had made for this emergency. His people believed that no ordinary bullet could kill him.

43

LE FERRIER

Battle, fire and earthquake could not destroy all the beauty of Christophe's capital Cap François, now Cap Haitien or simply "Le Cap." This picturesque city still reminds us that it was once the finest and richest in the West Indies.

The people had had enough of kings. They chose a good man by the name of Pétion to be president. They made Port-au-Prince the capital. Haiti became the first Negro republic.

A few decades ago divers thought they had found the anchor of Columbus's flagship, the *Santa Maria,* where it was wrecked east of Cap Haitien near Petit Anse. The anchor is now at a museum in Port-au-Prince except for one rusty iron sliver given in 1928 to the American aviator Colonel Charles A. Lindbergh when he surveyed routes for the first commercial airline in the West Indies.

Farther to the east a river called by the dreadful name of Massacre empties into the Atlantic. Upstream along its banks are fruits of every kind, birds and insects among plants growing as lush as anything in the Amazon Jungle.

Even at night in this jungle of Haiti life goes on. Armies of industrious ants are at work. Winged moths, praying mantises, beetles, mosquitoes, horrendous spiders, and giant cockroaches as big as grasshoppers are citizens of the night. Just before dawn a hush settles over the jungle. Then with the light a lilac orchid opens slowly into bloom. A ray of the sun makes a giant cobweb glitter, outlines on the trunk of a tree an iguana—a reptile left over from the age of dinosaurs, spotlights a yellow-breasted parrot, or perhaps picks out a pair of toucans with their ridiculously long beaks and gaudy plumage.

The Massacre River, according to story, got its name when Granados, a captain of Cortez's fleet, sailed up the river to find gold that never existed. He tortured the Indians, who in turn boarded his ship in the night and massacred the Spaniards.

Above Port-au-Prince in the mountains is the town Pétionville, named after the first president. People who have money live in Pétionville because it is cooler, and for the same reason others are moving now into Kenscoff, a town still higher in the mountains. When people leave their doors open at this height, clouds wander in and out of the houses.

In the late afternoon a never-ending line of women with produce baskets on their heads strides down through Kenscoff and Pétionville from higher in the mountains. Just outside the city limits of Port-au-Prince these women sleep beside their baskets under trees in the fields. But one tree none of them will sleep under is the "bomb" tree. The bomb tree grows long, tough black pods. When ripe, the pods curl open suddenly with a loud snap and violently throw out seeds in all directions.

When the sky lightens behind the mountains, the women eat some fruit from their baskets and put on their shoes. The law requires all people to wear shoes in Port-au-Prince, but since shoes are very expensive in Haiti, most country people carry their shoes and put them on only when they must. Once by the check point where a soldier examines what they are bringing into the capital, the women hurry to the Iron Market to secure a good place from which to sell.

In the late afternoon the same women start home again in chattering, laughing groups. Another line of women with heavily laden baskets will take their places on the following day.

To travel from one city to another most people take a bus. There are a few miles of a narrow-gauge rail line, but it does not go to many places. Buses have flat roofs with sides and backs open. Long, hard seats run from side to side. When a bus is not in use, the seats are taken out and stacked against a palm tree.

When a bus is ready to leave, it is filled to overflowing with people and trussed-up livestock. The roof is piled high with baskets and bundles tightly roped on. Amid shouts, laughter, screams of good-by and honking of horns, the bus starts with a jerk which snaps people back into their seats with more laughter. As it rumbles through the streets of the city, riders continue to wave and shout to friends and acquaintances. But once out in the country the passengers are busy holding on as the bus bangs and bumps over the unpaved roads. Unless it has just rained, everyone is soon enveloped in a cloud of thick, choking white dust.

In the country the typical house is something like the Cuban bohio. It has two rooms, with a steep tentlike roof thatched with palm leaves or covered with corrugated sheet iron. The walls are made of woven withes (green branches), all of them daubed with mud. This house is African, but what furniture there is, is European: a table, a few chairs, a bed, and not much else unless the owner has a little money.

Women prepare all the meals, and most of the dishes they cook are African: stews with meat and lots of peppers, and other foods fried in deep fat. The cooking is done outside or in a separate cooking shelter on a raised mud platform or on three stones supporting the stewpots.

Haitian farmers make fun out of working in the fields. In a country village farmers will form a working group called a *combite*. They combine to help a member clear his ground of underbrush and hoe his field for planting. In turn every member of the combite is helped. In a large combite as many as seventy-five men line up with their hoes ready. A drummer and a singer keep them working together until night and time to share a feast prepared by the wife of the owner of the field.

On higher, cooler fields farmers grow coffee in the shade of other trees. For one day only the coffee tree comes into bloom, smothered in blossoms. In time the tree produces berries. When ripe, the berries look like red cherries. Each berry yields two seeds, which have to be dried in the sun and then sorted.

If you ride back into the mountains, even the high mountains, you will find many people living in the little valleys. The villages look like African compounds. Goats, pigs, and children are everywhere. To keep the goats and pigs from running off into the jungle, the farmers lash long sticks about the animals' neck. The sticks catch in the undergrowth and turn the wandering animals back into the open spaces.

Haitians are very fond of the fruit from the mango tree, which is something like a very juicy plum with a very large seed. Bananas, avocados, oranges and limes also grow in the valleys.

Apart from the village and in a clearing in the jungle is to be found a special hut called a *houmfort*. It is a Voodoo prayer house, easy to pick out because the bleached skull of a horse perches on a pole in front of it.

Though most Haitians are Christians they believe in Voodoo, the ancient religion which the first African slaves brought with them. On Sunday morning a Haitian may go to the Christian church and in the afternoon pray to the Voodoo gods.

Around the houmfort the *hungan,* or priest, may draw secret symbols with yellow corn meal. At night men play the sacred drums, and the worshippers dance to the rhythms. Jazz came from these rhythms.

The Haitian or African drum is hollowed out of a tree trunk. Over the open end a fresh oxhide is pulled tight over wooden pegs fastened in the sides near the top. When the hide dries, it shrinks taut. The bigger the drum, the deeper the tone. The Haitian drummers are the most skillful in all the West Indies.

The hungans and the *mambus* (priestesses) believe they can foretell the future and perform miracles of healing. The Haitians think that bad spirits bring evil to the people and their crops, and that only the hungans can save them. Priests also preside at funerals.

Country Haitians turn a funeral into a festive holiday. The nearest relatives of a dead person give a banquet in his honor. They dress the dead person in his best clothes and seat him at the head of the table so that he can take part in the fun. When the feast is over, they put the body in a coffin and carry it to the cemetery. The hungan follows behind the coffin, zigzagging so the devil cannot catch up. On the way to the cemetery the women mourners stop at every crossroad, look anxiously on all sides and then run quickly over, "for everyone knows too that the devil waits for his victims at the crossroads."

Many Haitians believe in magic. That is why they do not like to be photographed. They think that a person can bring misfortune on his enemy by doing bad things to the enemy's picture.

In the other islands of the West Indies many people believe in Voodoo and magic, but they look to Haiti as the home of these mysteries. To them the Haitian hungans and mambus are the best.

For amusement the Haitian likes to play cards. Despite the heat some also enjoy European football, called soccer in the United States. But the spectator sport Haitians like best is cockfighting, where in a circular space, two roosters equipped with steel spurs fight each other to the death. Cockfighting is popular throughout the West Indies.

For the Haitian the most fun of all is dancing. Men, women and children love the beat of the drums. Once the drums begin to roll no one can keep still. Most Haitians do not have sweet singing voices; the drums sing for them. Haiti, above all else, is a land of rhythm. Rhythm enters into a man's work in the fields, his recreation, and into his innermost self—that part of his religion which came from Africa.

Ba-r-r-room, boom, boom, boom! Ba-r-r-room, boom, boom, boom! The drums are throbbing in the hills.

Santo Domingo

The Dominican Republic

ACROSS the mountains from Haiti is the Dominican Republic. Thirty years ago this was a poor, drowsy, underdeveloped country. Then one man, Dr. Rafael Leonidas Trujillo Molina, finding his country in rags, dressed it in fine clothes with splendid roads, new cities, modern factories, and luxury hotels. Everywhere in the lowlands are finely tailored fields, many of them cultivated with the latest machinery.

The Dominican landscape resembles that of Cuba except that it is more mountainous. Its modern dress is North American because Trujillo, once a United States marine, tried to copy all things American—that is, everything except the most important idea of all, democracy! His dictatorship came to a violent end when he was shot by rebels.

Trujillo came to power by driving out a man who tried to remain president beyond his elected term. A few weeks afterward a terrible hurricane almost destroyed Santo Domingo, the capital. Trujillo rebuilt the city in modern form and for a while it was called, in his honor, Ciudad Trujillo (City of Trujillo).

The hurricane of 1930 was not the first to attack the city. From the first settlement on Hispaniola, at La Isabela on the north coast, Columbus sent his brother Bartholomew to locate a better place for the capital of New Spain. Brother Bartholomew chose to build on the lower east bank of the Ozama River where it empties into the Caribbean Sea on the south side of the island. Shortly after settlers moved in, the new capital was lashed by winds of terrific force and flooded. As if that were not enough, gigantic armies of ants overran the remains. In desperation the survivors fled across the river to higher ground, where they began to construct a new city, part of which has lasted for nearly five hundred years.

The old Spanish buildings that remain were the finest in all of Spain's West Indian empire, for Santo Domingo was a city of European "firsts" in the Western Hemisphere: the first fort, the first alcazar, or palace, the first hospital, the first monastery, the first cathedral, and the first university. But the lure of gold across the sea in Mexico and Peru drained Santo Domingo of men.

COLUMBUS CATHEDRAL

ALCAZAR OF DIEGO COLUMBUS

Sensing the weakness of the city, the great English sea captain and daring pirate Sir Francis Drake carried Santo Domingo by storm and demanded ransom to spare the city, burning a section to show that he was serious. You can still visit the house where Drake stayed until the money was paid by the frightened citizens. It is called the Cord House because of a piece of carved rope decoration over the front door. Built in 1504, it is the oldest house standing in the West Indies.

Among the interesting places to visit in the capital is the cathedral, the oldest and finest in all the islands. The cathedral is imposing and simple, built the way the Spaniards built at home in Spain. By contrast the tomb of Columbus inside the cathedral has too many decorations. Most people agree that the bones inside the tomb actually are those of the great navigator.

53

Another fine old building is called Columbus Castle, or just the Alcazar. It was the home of Diego Columbus, son of the great explorer. Because of his father's fame, Diego was received well at court, and when he grew up, he married Doña Maria de Toledo, a relative of the queen of Spain. Diego was appointed governor of all of New Spain in the West Indies, and after a stay in the Cord House until his new home was ready, he moved into the Alcazar. Fortunately Trujillo restored this old medieval palace, and today it is the finest Spanish building in the West Indies that isn't a church.

Santo Domingo presents the greatest contrast to Port-au-Prince. Built on flat land, it spreads out into wide, tree-lined avenues with parks and many new public buildings. Where the capital faces the Caribbean Sea, the Avenue George Washington runs along the waterfront.

The Spaniards built walls around Santo Domingo. As the city grew, it burst through these barriers and people tore down most of the walls because they were in the way. As a souvenir of old Spanish days the government left the two finest of the city gates, Puerta de la Misericordia (Mercy Gate), and Puerta del Conde (Count Gate).

The Count Gate got its name, according to an old story, from Count Peñalva, who was such a fine swordsman that all alone he turned back a British landing force. Another story about the Count Gate, which you can believe, is that in 1844, from the top of the gate, Juan Pablo Duarte read a declaration of independence freeing Santo Domingo from Haitian rule. Some years later Santo Domingo tried to join the United States but our government did not accept the offer.

The new city west of the Count Gate has modern business houses, stores and new homes. East of the city is a nice white sand beach called Boca Chica. Although Santo Domingo is one of the big cities of the West Indies, it is only about a third the size of Havana.

As in Cuba, sugar is a very important crop. The Spaniards brought sugar cane across the Atlantic Ocean from the Canary Islands and planted it first in Santo Domingo. As in other islands, they tried to enslave the gentle Arawak Indians to work their sugar plantations and when the red men died, they brought in Negroes in their place.

The only way to travel in the Dominican Republic is by bus or auto. Most of the railroads lead directly to the sugar centrals, one of which, Central

Rio Haina, is the largest in the world. But there are a number of splendid roads, many of them through very beautiful country. The road from Santiago to its seaport, Puerto Plata, is the most beautiful. It climbs across rugged forests with occasional tiny patches of cleared fields carved out of the woods. Here the people live in bohios. As your auto crosses the mounains to the coast, you pass donkeys carrying enormous loads of red-clay pottery or bales of tobacco, see girls loaded down with sisal fiber for making rope, and boys balancing stems of bananas on their heads. Or you may catch up with the Dominican bread wagon—a small donkey nearly hidden by huge twin barrels filled with loaves of bread.

The Haitian plain called the Cul de Sac cuts through the mountains and crosses the border of the Dominican Republic, sinking in its deepest part to Lake Enriquillo, whose surface is a hundred and fifty feet below sea level. Lake Enriquillo is salt. The surface of the water is slimy. And even though there are rain jungles in other places, the shores of this lake are so dry that cactus grows there. As in the southwestern United States, there are ancient Indian remains and petrified trees, which show that the region was not always dry.

Rio Haina

Southeast of Lake Enriquillo on the coast of Barahona rises a whole mountain of nearly pure salt three hundred and fifty feet high. North of the lake are the Cibao Mountains, so lofty that even here in the tropics the snow falls on them periodically. The highest is 10,417 feet in height, or nearly twice as high as Mount Washington in New England. Many of the foothills and mountains have wet and dry sides, with jungle on the lower slopes of the wet side and campeche (logwood) brush on the dry. Pines and cactus are on opposite sides, all because the trade winds blow the rain clouds steadily from one direction.

As in Cuba, tobacco and coffee are important crops, but in the Dominican Republic cacao is also a major product. Chocolate comes from the cacao bean. The plant came from South and Central America and Mexico, and cacao was served originally by the Aztecs as a drink. When the Spaniards conquered Mexico, they brought the drink to Spain. Mixed with cinnamon it became, and still is, the most popular hot drink. To satisfy the increasing demand the Spanish started vast cacao plantations in Santo Domingo.

Cacao plantations yield two crops a year from trees which could grow forty feet high but are trimmed to fifteen or twenty feet to make the harvest easier. The beans come from the seeds of a fifteen-inch leathery pod. Like coffee beans, they are dried in the sun and then roasted to crack off the outer shell. From the inner piece, called a nib, machinery presses out cocoa butter, useful in the manufacture of certain medical supplies. What is left is dried and ground into powder to become chocolate.

Although the Dominican Republic is several times larger than Haiti, the two and a half million population of this Spanish-speaking country is a million less than its neighbor across the mountains. And since the Dominican Republic has much fertile land with room for more people, it has opened its door to persons who want to leave their own homelands and start life over again. At Sosúa on the north coast there is a Jewish colony. In some places you can see Japanese children on their way to school. Spaniards from the overthrown Spanish Republic found a place to live in the Dominican Republic where they could go into cattle farming on the higher, cooler lands.

Cacao Pods

There is still room for many more people, for almost two thirds of the country is covered with forests, the way Cuba was two hundred years ago. Mahogany is the national tree, but there are other usable woods such as pine, oak and ebony. The Spaniards found small deposits of gold, which is still being mined. Iron and bauxite have been found in considerable quantities, but fuel in the form of coal and oil is scarce. The several unnavigable rivers flowing down from the mountains could furnish electric power to solve this difficulty.

Like other West Indians the Dominicans like cockfighting, but they like baseball, too. If you watch a night game in the capital and sit in the stands crowded with *fanáticos* under the great banks of lights turning the night into day, you think that you are somewhere in the United States. And you can understand much of what the *fanáticos* are yelling, for the language of baseball is English.

Horse shows and cattle shows are popular, too. Like the Cubans, the Dominicans enjoy the Sunday evening *paseo*. As they sit in a park or walk round and round a central bandstand, families like to visit and listen to popular music in the soft tropical night.

The predominant color of the West Indies is green, because these are hot and rainy lands. But there are other colors. Cement town houses are painted in pastel shades of cream, blue, purple and pink. Although the leaves of the trees do not change into brilliant warm colors in the fall, the glorious *flamboyan* (flame) tree turns a lobster-red in the spring, and the luxuriant bougainvillaea vine blossoms riotously in shades of red and red-purple.

In Spanish lands there is a very ancient friendly custom. If on entering a house you admire an object, your host will say, *"A la orden!"* which means, "It's yours!" Of course, it would not be polite to accept the article as a gift unless your host insists, but there is one gift that you can accept: friendship.

Puerto Rico

"IF there are a lot of Americans, run! If there are few, hide! If there are none, fight!"

This comedy command was given by a Spanish officer to his men when United States forces under General Nelson Miles landed on Puerto Rico in 1898. The relations between the islanders and the mother country were so bad that the Puerto Ricans hardly lifted a finger to help their Spanish rulers.

Today Puerto Rico is virtually part of the United States. Thousands of American soldiers and their families live in great military bases on the island. There are American-looking buildings, Florida-like hotels, big factories, supermarkets, fifteen hundred miles of fine highways, baseball and basketball teams, and even drum majorettes. In the homes and in the country districts some of the Spanish customs linger on, and if you went to school on the island, you would have to study Spanish with your regular subjects.

There are as many people on this island as in the Dominican Republic, which is several times larger than Puerto Rico. There are so many that thousands of them come to the United States every year to find work. They can come because they are United States citizens.

On his second voyage to the New World, Columbus discovered Puerto Rico. "A fair land" he found the island with its central ridge of mountains and its flatter coastal areas. Colonists followed quickly. Ponce de León was the first governor. Since he paid a famous visit to Florida in search of the Fountain of Youth, he has also been called the first Puerto Rican emigrant to the United States.

The Spaniards named the island after San Juan Bautista (Saint John the Baptist). The fine natural harbor on the north shore facing the Atlantic Ocean they called Puerto Rico (Rich Port). Today the names are reversed. The big port city is San Juan and the island is Puerto Rico.

As they did in Santo Domingo and Havana, the Spaniards built walls around San Juan, which occupies a small island. They built another Morro Castle on the tip end of the island where the Spanish treasure ships used to enter the harbor. San Juan has been called the Gibraltar of the Western world. The massive stone walls turned back just about everybody and everything: pirates, English, French and Dutch men-of-war, even shots and shells fired by American warships in the Spanish-American War. Still standing are most of the city walls, Morro Castle, and the Fortaleza, which is something like an alcazar. There the governor lives. The original island city has many old Spanish buildings. San Juan Island is hilly; in some places the streets are flights of steps. In other parts the narrow streets wind, twist, and climb, with houses built wall to wall, their front doors opening onto the narrow sidewalks. Often it is possible to walk from roof to roof.

Old San Juan is connected by bridges to the mainland, where buildings become more modern the farther they are from the old city. San Juan is growing so fast it has swallowed up the nearby towns of Santurce, Hato Rey, and even Río Piedras seven and a half miles away.

For a long time there have been ties between Puerto Rico and the United States. In 1777 when our Revolutionary War was in full swing, two American ships, the *Endawock* and the *Henry*, running away from the British frigate *Glasgow*, found safety in the Puerto Rican seaport of Mayagüez. To pro-

HAULING SUGAR CANE

tect the ships the Puerto Ricans quickly raised the Spanish flag over them and saved the crews from capture. Thus the islanders were among the very first to recognize the independence of our original Thirteen Colonies.

The Spaniards brought sugar early to Puerto Rico. Since the islanders were the most loyal of all Spain's West Indian peoples, the Puerto Ricans were permitted to sell sugar directly to the rest of the world, instead of shipping it first to Spain the way Cuba and Santo Domingo had to do.

In Spanish days this island was the poorest of the colonies. When the Spaniards killed off the Arawak Indians by trying to make them work on the sugar plantations, the masters were not rich enough to import Negro slaves in very great numbers. As one by one Spain's other colonies became independent, white families still loyal to Spain resettled in Puerto Rico. To-day more native white people live in Puerto Rico than anywhere else in the West Indies.

Puerto Ricans were content to be ruled by Spain until the last half of the nineteenth century. Then Spain tried to restrict the islanders' liberty. They threw Puerto Rican leaders in jail and stopped trade with the United States. When the Spanish-American War came, Puerto Ricans were happy to see the Spaniards go.

At first under American rule, the President of the United States appointed American governors to rule Puerto Rico. In 1946 President Truman made Jesús Pinero governor, the first Puerto Rican to hold that office. Two years later the United States allowed the islanders to draw up a constitution for self-government and to elect their own governor.

Since the island was overpopulated, many of the people lived in great poverty, especially in two areas in San Juan, El Fanguito (the Little Mudhole) and La Perla (the Pearl), which is anything but a pearl. Fortunately the climate, varying between 70 degrees and 85 degrees Fahrenheit, is very mild. No one ever suffers from the cold. People can spend a great deal of time out of doors. The new Puerto Rican government is doing much to get rid of the bad living areas by persuading foreign businessmen to locate new factories on the island, so that people can have work, and by building thousands of new houses for families living in the poor districts.

Puerto Ricans make money from sugar, coffee and tobacco, just like the Cubans and Dominicans. They distill more rum than do the people of any other island.

Spanish customs are more noticeable in the other towns on the island than in San Juan. The country people, *jíbaros*, love festivals and parties. They give a party when a member of the family goes away or when he returns, or for Grandfather or Grandmother on his or her saint's day. They make much of the Christmas season, which lasts from Christmas Eve until Twelfth-night (January 6). On Christmas they give gifts, and also on Twelfth-night

in remembrance of the gifts given to the Christ Child by the Three Kings.

On January 5 children put dishes of grass and corn under their beds for the camels of the Wise Men. In the morning the children find the food gone and gifts in its place. At Christmastime the *parrandas* (strolling minstrels) play and sing, and are invited into all houses. They expect to be served *morcillas* (three kinds of sausages), *arroz con dulce* (rice pudding), *pasteles* (cakes), and *lechón asada* (roast pig), which all Spanish West Indians love to eat.

Almost every day in Puerto Rico a fiesta is held somewhere in honor of some saint. Most fiestas are little carnivals set up for the day with Ferris wheel, merry-go-round, donkey rides, candy, roast pork, and dancing which lasts all night. Then, as in most of the islands, there is "carnival," the great merrymaking period just before the beginning of Lent.

The Caribbean National Forest, at a spot called El Yunque (the Anvil), is a marvelous place to visit, about forty miles from San Juan into the central mountains. On the way you can see the beautiful campus of the University of Puerto Rico. If you are hungry, there are roast-pork stands beside the road like the hot-dog stands in the United States. El Yunque is like a huge natural greenhouse—botanists call it a rain jungle—with tree ferns so high they arch clear over the roadway.

Brightly colored plants and flowers line the sides of Route One leading across the island to Ponce, the second largest city. In the fields grow giant pineapples, some weighing as much as fifteen pounds. Ponce is a Spanish town with many modern business buildings. The *parque de bombas* (firehouse) is the gayest building in the West Indies. The parque screams with red, black and white stripes, squares and fanlike decorations. A *bomba* is a pump. There are real fire engines in the parque, too.

63

Two places where you can see the old Puerto Rico are San Germán, an inland town, and Mayagüez, the seaport on the west coast where the American ships took shelter in 1777. Even here modern Puerto Rico is building factories.

Many Puerto Ricans want the island to become the fifty-first state, others want it to be an independent country, but most people want to go on the way they are, governing themselves and enjoying United States citizenship.

The Virgin Islands

COLUMBUS named a whole host of smaller islands and cays east of Puerto Rico after Saint Ursula and eleven thousand other virgins who had set out to pray at Rome, and had all been killed by the Huns besieging Cologne.

Of course there are not eleven thousand islands, really not many more than fifty. Today the Virgin Islands are owned by England and the United States. The most important, St. Thomas, St. Croix, and St. John, belong to the United States. Tourists like to visit them in the winter, so they can swim, play tennis, go fishing, or just loaf.

The Spaniards, who brought sugar cane to the Virgin Islands, did not stay long, and the Danes took their places, building the town Charlotte Amalie and a fort on St. Thomas. Then Denmark sold the islands to the United States during World War I.

The islands have high, rolling hills and many bays that look as though they had been punched out by a giant cooky cutter. On one of these bays is Christiansted, the capital of St. Croix. It has a very beautiful harbor with many perfectly preserved houses and other buildings that are at least two hundred years old.

On the other side of St. Croix there is a gingerbread town. Frederiksted was burned down completely in 1878. When the townspeople rebuilt, they loaded the new wooden houses with curlicue decorations just to be in style. The fire did not destroy the fort, with its walls four feet thick. Here in Frederiksted the man whose face is on the United States ten-dollar bill, Alexander Hamilton, managed a trading warehouse at the age of fourteen. Although Hamilton was born in Nevis, his mother brought him to Frederiksted when he was ten.

There is a story told about St. John's Island that may or may not be true. In Danish days sugar cane almost covered the island. The white masters were so cruel that in 1733 the Negro slaves revolted and wiped out the whites. French soldiers coming in to put down the uprising backed the slaves to the cliff at Mary's Point. Rather than be captured, the Negroes jumped to their death in the sea. Their ghosts are supposed to haunt the point.

St. Thomas, second largest of the Virgin Islands, has the pretty seaport with the woman's name, Charlotte Amalie. The town starts at the water's edge and climbs part way up into the hills. The famous pirate Blackbeard is said to have made the massive round fort in Charlotte Amalie his castle.

Blackbeard wore his whiskers braided and had fourteen wives. For fun he used to take his friends into the hold of his ship and burn sulphur matches to see who could stand the fumes longest. Stevenson borrowed the name of Blackbeard's chief gunner, Israel Hands, for one of his pirates in *Treasure Island*.

Now the pirates have gone, but the beautiful islands remain.

Navassa

MOST people have never heard of the island of Navassa, and even the few who have probably would not know about the island if a murder had not taken place there. It is only by chance that Navassa belongs to the United States, and it costs money to own the island.

Navassa is a dangerous two-mile-long cliff with sharp reefs, standing in a heavily traveled sea lane between Cuba, Haiti and Jamaica. When Columbus, on his fourth and last voyage, was wrecked off St. Ann's Bay, Jamaica, he sent Diego Méndez, a daredevil captain, to Hispaniola for help, in a dugout canoe with an Indian crew.

After a day or so the Indians ran out of food and water, and threatened Méndez. But then they blundered on Navassa, where they found rain pools of water collected in the rocks, and where they killed sea birds for food. Méndez reached Hispaniola safely.

For three hundred and fifty-three years Navassa stood forgotten except when some unfortunate ship smashed into its rocks. One calm day in 1856 a young man by the name of Peter Duncan found Navassa again, made a tricky landing, explored the island, and planted an American flag on it. When he returned home to the United States he notified the government that he had claimed Navassa for it. Duncan noted that there was rich fertilizer called guano on the island. Guano is the droppings of birds.

Duncan returned with men to harvest the fertilizer. By 1889 there were as many as a hundred and fifty men there working under a superintendent. But in that year the weather turned much hotter than usual. Water and supplies ran low and the men were lonely. Tempers flashed, a riot broke out, and when the superintendent tried to quiet the mutineers, he was murdered.

Later the United States built a lighthouse on the island. Several years ago the light was equipped with automatic electrical controls, relieving the lighthouse keeper of his lonely job.

Ships twenty-five miles away can see the light. It sits on top of a 162-foot tower standing on the highest part of the island, a total of 395 feet above sea level. Captains of ships traveling to the West Indies, North and South America, and the Panama Canal are all glad that Peter Duncan claimed this little ragged piece of rock for the United States.

The Leeward Islands

THE West Indies seem an almost endless chain of islands. The chain begins west of Florida, stretches eastward for over fifteen hundred miles and then curls its tail another fifteen hundred miles, first southward and then westward, flicking the north coast of South America. The large islands in the north are called the Greater Antilles, while the curling tail is known as the Lesser Antilles. Originally "Antilles" was the name of a mythical group of islands supposedly lying between Africa and India. After Columbus's discovery, people called the West Indies the Antilles.

There are a bewildering number of islands in the Lesser Antilles. Most of these are divided into two groups; the northern ones are known as the Leeward Islands and the southern ones as the Windward Islands. "Lee" means protected from the wind, the opposite of "windward," the side which catches the wind.

The Dutch island Saba is in the Leeward group, not very far southeast of the Virgin Islands. You can't sail up to the dock or land on an airfield the way you can at most islands. Saba Islanders run out their surfboat with the long oars, take you and your luggage over the side from a steamer, and then hurry their boat through crashing breakers onto a tiny strip of shingle beach. Up above, Saba towers three thousand feet in the air, so high that it usually sits with its head in the clouds.

Saba, rising abruptly from the sea, is an extinct volcano five miles in circumference. The capital and main settlement, known by the elegant name of Bottom, is on the floor of the crater eight hundred feet up. A few years ago the only way to reach Bottom was by a flight of stairs cut into the rock. The Sabans refer to it as "the Ladder," a ladder with over five hundred steps.

Formerly everything had to be carried up the Ladder into this hawk's nest: food, lumber, furniture, even pianos. The Sabans used to be very skillful at building boats. They packed all the materials up the Ladder, shaped the hulls near the head of it, and then performed the almost incredible feat of lowering the boats over the face of the cliffs.

The few visitors who come to Saba now land at a strip called Fort Bay. From here a narrow corkscrew road that took five years to build makes it possible to ride to Bottom in a jeep. When you reach Bottom, you rub your eyes in amazement. Here is a Dutch village of neat white houses and red tile roofs. You expect to hear people talking Dutch, but the natives speak English. And then you learn one thing right off about the Lesser Antilles: the Spaniards, English, French, Danes, and Dutch have fought over these islands for three hundred years, and these parcels of land have changed hands so many times that the natives speak English where they ought to speak Dutch, French where they ought to speak English, and so on.

Why do people want to live on Saba? There is very little soil for gardens. Above Bottom there are one small banana plantation and two smaller villages one above another, Windwardside and Hellsgate. If you dropped something out of the front window at Hellsgate, you would have to go down twenty-four hundred feet to pick it up. While the men are away working in the oil refineries at Aruba and Curaçao, the women make lace at home.

Many of the Leeward Islands look alike. They have strips of beach bordered by groves of coconut palms. Back from the shore, sugar cane follows the valleys into the hills and low mountains. Where there is a natural harbor, you will find a town of white houses with hibiscus and bougainvillaea trailing over white balconies. Red roofs stand out brilliantly from the prevailing green.

If you are flying, the islands come quickly like steppingstones. Sint (St.) Eustatius (Dutch), with its volcanic cone, is important only because of its memories. The cannon of Fort Oranje were the first to salute a vessel from the Thirteen Colonies that were to become the United States. In retaliation the English wrecked the town, much of which is still in ruins.

Sint Maarten, or St. Martin, depending on whether you land on the Dutch or the French side of this hilly island, is a splendid example of two different peoples getting along well together in a small space. For a living, both sides fish and look after tourists. In French-ruled St. Barts, short for Saint-Barthél-

Windwardside

emy, the older women dress in Norman-French peasant costumes but speak English. Their ancestors were Swedes.

The next cluster of islands—St. Kitts, Nevis, Montserrat, and Redonda—even though named by the Spanish are now all English. The silhouette of St. Kitts looked to Columbus like St. Christopher carrying the Christ child. Clouds playing tag around the great mountain peak of Nevis (thirty-six hundred feet high) made it appear covered with snow. Hence the original name Nieve, which is Spanish for snow. The rugged, mountainous Montserrat looked similar to the mountains in back of Barcelona. And Redonda means "round" in Spanish.

Even though no one lives on bare and rocky Redonda, the island has a king. Back in 1865 Matthew Shiel had eight daughters. Then a son was born. Shiel was so happy that he thought his son Matthew Phipps Shiel ought to have a kingdom. When the boy was fifteen years old, his father took him and a minister to Redonda. They crowned Matthew Phipps king—King Felipe I. The British Colonial Office actually recognized Shiel as king. King Felipe I grew up in London to be the famous author M. P. Shiel. When he died in 1947, leaving no son, he passed the title on to a friend.

71

On St. Kitts the natives say that long ago volcanic Mount Misery "blew its top," and the top is Brimstone Hill. Fort George, crowning Brimstone Hill, is so massive that it makes you think of Christophe's citadel in Haiti. The French held St. Kitts for a time and brought in monkeys as pets. When they left, the monkeys ran wild. People still catch them for pets on Monkey Hill.

Long ago it was quite fashionable for people to go to Nevis for their health, soaking in the natural hot baths at the Bath House Hotel on the outskirts of Charlestown. Parts of Charlestown, especially around the hotel, still show the effects of an earthquake, but the ruins are fascinating. Charlestown and another town called Newcastle need only costumes on the people to look as they did a hundred and fifty years ago. Alexander Hamilton was born in Nevis, and Horatio Nelson, England's greatest admiral, married a pretty young lady in Fig Tree Church near Charlestown.

Stone windmill towers on Montserrat show how sugar once was ground. You can visit a volcano where milky white water seethes and steams. The people hunt *crapauds*—frogs as big as chickens—for food.

Antigua, named by Columbus after a church in Sevilla, Spain, is British. People think that a great amount of rain falls on all West Indian islands, but there are dry spots, and Antigua is one. Its hills are not high enough to make clouds drop rain. This dryness in the winter months is attracting more and more American tourists.

About a mile from Antigua's capital, St. John's, is a well-protected anchorage called English Harbor. One hundred and fifty years ago it was the most important British naval base in the Western Hemisphere. Recently the Antiguans have restored English Harbor so perfectly that one almost expects to meet Admiral Nelson in command again.

The best dancers in the entire West Indies live on Antigua. Negroes put on colorful costumes and masks to dance on the beach. Originally these dances came from Africa in slave days. In one typical dance a clown with a rawhide whip chases another. The long whip comes excitingly close, but it does not quite touch.

In the eighteenth century the English and French, as part of their struggle for world empire, fought over the sugar-rich West Indies. In sight of the large British island of Dominica, which is halfway between the Leeward and Windward groups, occurred one of the world's greatest naval battles. The Battle of the Saints takes its name from the Isles of the Saints nearby. The English won, but the French still kept their two big islands, Guadeloupe to the north of Dominica and Martinique to the south.

Dominica, with mountain ridge after mountain ridge, is so high that rain falls frequently to make lush jungles. Here the last real survivors of the Carib Indians live. Their village has changed little in hundreds of years. The coming of the Spaniards stopped the northern movement of the warlike Caribs, who were conquering the West Indies island by island from the original settlers, the Arawaks. From them the Caribbean Sea got its name.

Battle of the Saints

The Windward Islands

OF the two big French islands, Martinique is by far the more interesting. It is exactly what a typical tropical island ought to be, warm, rainy, and lush, with green mountains. Unlike Guadeloupe, it is not just another sugar island with a volcanic cone, but an island with a lot of things to talk about: the deadly fer-de-lance, the Emperor Napoleon's wife, a rock that was once a ship in the British Navy, a ruined city, and the terrible Mont Pelée.

Afraid that the slaves on their own islands might revolt, the English protected French planters and their plantations on Martinique from destruction during the French Revolution. And to keep slaves from running away, planters imported a deadly snake, the fer-de-lance, and loosed it in the jungles. The immensely wealthy planters kept old Fort-de-France as the capital but built St. Pierre, a show town, to the north, at the water's edge in a crescent of hills under the shadow of Mont Pelée, towering four thousand feet high.

St. Pierre was a beautiful city of forty thousand people. It had an imposing cathedral, an elegant opera house, and many splendid mansions filled with fine furnishings, lots of them priceless antiques. The houses were very French, with red tile roofs steeply pitched to carry off the heavy tropical rains.

Palms, bougainvillaea, and many other graceful plants added to the beauty of St. Pierre. Down from the hills, water ran in little side channels in the streets to cool the air, in the way the Moors had planned centuries ago for their palaces in Spain. St. Pierre was a busy port, too. Ships brought luxuries for the planters and took away sugar, rum, coffee, and vanilla.

Suddenly on the morning of May 8, 1902, the world came to an end for St. Pierre. With two quick, terrific explosions Mont Pelée split wide open. A violent cloud of fire and gas roared into and over the city. In a few seconds the blast destroyed buildings, snuffed out lives, broiled the ships and their crews in the harbor, and even boiled those who jumped overboard into the water. Two ships with badly burned survivors reached Fort-de-France. Of the forty thousand within the city one man only did not die. He, a criminal awaiting execution, was in a dungeon so deep that fire and gas passed over him harmlessly.

Today a small ramshackle town occupies part of the site of St. Pierre, but mostly ruins are left, ruins like those of the old Roman city of Pompeii.

In Fort-de-France a gleaming marble statue to the beautiful heroine of Martinique proclaims that Joséphine de la Pagerie, a planter's daughter born on the island, became Empress of France. Her first husband, Alexander de Beauharnais, had been guillotined in the Revolution. The great Napoleon fell in love with the widow Josephine and married her.

Some miles south of Fort-de-France, British naval vessels dip their colors by way of salute to a rocky island, not much bigger than an old ship of the line, known as His Majesty's Ship Diamond Rock. In 1804, to harass French shipping, English sailors and marines dragged five cannon to the two-hundred-foot top. Finally, after seventeen months of heroic resistance and with ammunition running low, the English surrendered.

Martinique

There are many other things to see in Martinique: bamboo houses with thatch roofs, a dry region on the very southern tip with deposits of salt and a petrified "forest" something like that in the Dominican Republic, rain jungles with giant ferns, deep steep-sided canyons called gorges, swift rivers, and waterfalls.

South of Martinique the British have a corner of the Windward Islands. St. Lucia, called the Pearl of the Lesser Antilles, boasts a drive-in volcano called La Soufrière. "Soufrière" means volcano in French.

If you want to, you can walk right into Soufrière's crater. You won't burn yourself if you stay out of the hot pools, because old Soufrière is just sputtering and letting off steam like the geysers in Yellowstone National Park in the United States. One time when the French owned the island, soldiers made a series of stone bathtubs, which could be filled with volcanic hot water. The tubs are still usable and the plumbing still works.

Soufrière the volcano is just behind Soufrière the little fishing port. As gateposts to Soufrière rise the two most famous peaks in the West Indies. Gros Piton and Petit Piton are volcanic plugs formed by lava that tried to reach the earth's surface but failed. When the softer earth washed away, the hard peaks were left.

Castries, the deepwater port of St. Lucia, is not as big as it looks from the surrounding hills. Every time Castries burned, the inhabitants did not bother to pull down the ruins, but built new structures right alongside the broken walls. Tropical plants quickly healed the fire-burned look.

Most of the islands of the Lesser Antilles are volcanic in origin. On British-owned St. Vincent another Soufrière blew up at the same time as Mont Pelée and killed many people. In ages past when lava reached the surface, the air cooled it so quickly the lava became brittle and soon broke down into very rich soil. To keep the soil from washing away, the farmers of this island terraced the mountainsides, which rise to a peak of four thousand feet. Looking more like a twin to Tahiti in the South Pacific than a West Indian island, St. Vincent grows sugar and has a near monopoly on the arrowroot plant. Fine starches used in crackers, baby food, and canned soup come from St. Vincent arrowroot.

A breadfruit tree growing in the botanical garden at Kingstown, the capital, connects St. Vincent with Tahiti. To supply cheap food for slaves, Captain Bligh of *Mutiny on the Bounty* fame, on his second attempt, brought seedlings of the plant from Tahiti. The present tree has grown from one of the seedlings. The breadfruit tree, reaching heights of thirty to forty feet, bears a fruit that looks like an eight-inch melon. Baked breadfruit tastes like potato, and when mixed with milk and sugar, it becomes a delicious pudding. Dried, it can be ground into flour. People make furniture and canoes from the wood and use the sap for glue.

If Captain Bligh could sail into Kingstown today, he would find that the port had changed little since his first visit. The islanders still go out in rowing craft with old-time whaling gear to catch a small whale they call "the big black fish."

Petit Piton

Barbados, the easternmost island of the West Indies, often called Little England, is truly very British with its gently rolling hills and its English houses, churches and customs—until you catch the familiar smell of crushed sugar cane and molasses. As in the other islands of the Windward group, the Atlantic, driven by the trade winds, eternally smashes against the east coast, leaving the westward side with calm waters and fine beaches that are favorites with aqualung and snorkel fans.

The most photographed police in the West Indies are the nattily dressed city officers of Bridgetown, capital and chief port of Barbados. To this day the harbor police dress like Nelson's seamen, who freed Barbados from a costly French blockade. A sign on a house in Bridgetown says George Washington lived here. This may or may not be, but before he became great, Washington brought his brother Laurence to the island to recover from tuberculosis.

One of the many fine estate houses outside Bridgetown belonged many years ago to a man named Sam Lord. He is said to have lured ships to destruction on the rocks by placing lanterns in the trees on the shore. Ship captains thought they were coming into port. Lord, however, stole their cargoes and murdered survivors.

Barbados is shaped like a teardrop, and at the very end of the tip, which points north, there are green and purple sea caves with many-colored animal flowers. The sea fills the caves at high tide, but at low tide you can walk inside to look at the pools with the strange flowers. Point a finger at a flower and it folds its petals immediately, sinking back into the sand. The bright colors attract prey for the flower's dinner.

A hundred or so little steppingstone islands south of St. Vincent, called The Grenadines, have fine beaches and are famed for oysters growing on trees. The mangrove tree puts down roots wherever it feels like it, even in water and oyster beds. You can break off a root and bring up a delicious cluster of oysters.

Green, wooded hills, low mountains, a lake, the Grand Etang, fifteen hundred feet up in an extinct volcano, sparkling beaches, and St. George, a port with water so deep ocean liners can tie up at the old docks, make Grenada the most beautiful small island in the West Indies. Columbus, returning today, would find it a true spice island. Cinnamon, bayberry, vanilla, ginger, and nutmeg make money for the natives. Nutmeg trees, like cacao trees, grow best in deep shade. When ripe, nutmeg pods are rich yellow on the outside and scarlet-lined on the inside. The women who pick the ripe pods like to wear bright-colored dresses.

Trinidad

THE strange, exotic island of Trinidad, just fifteen miles from South America and a little over half the size of Puerto Rico, is a mixture of the East Indies and West Indies. One third of the six hundred thousand inhabitants came as immigrants, or their parents did, from Asia. There are Hindu temples and houses. Some people wear turbans and saris, and there are Mohammedans with fezzes on their heads. Zebus—cattle from India that can stand the heat—plow the rice fields and water buffaloes haul sugar cane to rail sidings.

People often call Trinidad the "asphalt and carnival" island. Everybody celebrates carnival in the West Indies, but the torrent of mirth released in Port of Spain the Monday and Tuesday before the beginning of Lent is tremendous. Steel bands and calypso singers give a special "beat" to the celebration.

Someone discovered that by taking steel oil drums—Trinidad has plenty of them, being the third largest oil producer in the British Commonwealth —and by cutting the gasoline containers off at different lengths, he could make a series of drums that would play as many as twenty-three separate notes. Fifteen or more people make up a band, each with a separate drum, painted and hung from the shoulders by straps.

Calypso singers band together and put up a tent on a vacant lot. Inside are seats for spectators, and a small stage with a five-piece steel band. Introduced by a master of ceremonies, each singer comes out in turn and with humor and melody makes up stories in verse and song about news events, famous people, friends or the other singers. The audience will listen gleefully for hours.

Washington, D.C., had the first asphalt-paved streets in the United States and the tar came from the great lake of pure asphalt on Trinidad. You can walk on the lake surface, but if you should try to stay in one spot too long, the lake would swallow you up the way it engulfed prehistoric animals thousands of years ago.

Laborers using heavy picks chop out big chunks of asphalt and load them into little cars, which run on a narrow-gauge track that has to be moved every few days lest it sink out of sight in the tar. Taken to the refinery, the chunks of asphalt are melted and poured into barrels and shipped to distant countries to pave city streets. After four days the lake levels off again, filling up the holes dug by man. Digging constantly for seventy-two years, man has lowered the lake only thirty-eight feet, and the lake is still two hundred and fifty feet deep.

Steel
Drums

In the wonderful Botanic Garden of Port of Spain many scents perfume the air from flowers, bay leaves, camphor, and eucalyptus. The trees are fantastic. The monkeypot tree has roots that pop in and out of the ground, twisting like snakes for yards around the tree. Then there is the *coco de mer* (double coconut), bearing the world's biggest seeds, weighing up to fifty pounds. The cable vine is a queer bit of nature; it can grow right through the trunk of a tree. Sausage trees, sacred Buddhist fig trees, Brazil nuts, Ceylon willows, samans, tamarinds, whose seeds make a pleasant drink, and many others will fascinate you for hours.

Leaving the island, one can see why it was called Trinidad by Columbus. The three main mountain peaks reminded him of the Holy Trinity. The Carib Indians called the island Iere, or "Land of the Humming Bird."

The small island of Tobago's chief claim to fame is that it might have been and could have been, from its landscape, the island Defoe had in mind when he wrote *The Life and Adventures of Robinson Crusoe*. On very nearby Little Tobago one can visit the only bird of paradise sanctuary in the Western Hemisphere.

Scattered westward are a number of islands, which belong to Venezuela. Margarita, the largest, is a pearl island. In the seaport of Porlamar one can see whole tubs and baskets of pearls for sale. Divers bring up pearls from oyster beds, but not from the kind of oysters you eat. Irritated by a grain of sand inside his shell, an oyster covers it over with many layers of a substance he himself makes, until it becomes a ball. The ball is a pearl.

La Asunción, the capital of Nueva Esparta, looks like a small town in Spain. Blanquilla and Tortuga also have pearl divers. The Spaniards found many islands with turtles swimming around them to which they gave the Spanish name for turtle, *tortuga*. There are the Dry Tortugas off Florida, the buccaneer island off Haiti, the Cayman Islands, first called Las Tortugas, and this Venezuelan island.

Willemstad

The ABC Islands

THE ABC Islands, Aruba, Bonaire and Curaçao, all Dutch-owned, are the end of the tail formed by the Lesser Antilles. Aruba and Curaçao are two of the most valuable small islands on earth, because on them are the world's largest oil refineries. The oil comes from Venezuela, which has one of the richest oil fields in the world. Bonaire is the poor sister, but an interesting place to visit. Offshore fishing is excellent and you can examine some very ancient Indian carvings on the walls of a grotto (cave) called Boca Onima. If you are on Bonaire in May and June you can see and photograph great flocks of pink flamingos nesting—a very rare sight.

Almost every West Indian travel booklet has a picture of the seventeenth-century-Holland houses on the waterfront at Willemstad, capital and chief port of Curaçao. As in Amsterdam, people can go on board a floating market. And in Willemstad is the most famous bridge in the West Indies. It floats on twelve big pontoons! When a ship wants to enter the harbor, the Queen Emma floating bridge can be swung to one side. One statue in town seems familiar: Peter Stuyvesant, he of the peg leg, was governor of Curaçao before he went to New York.

From the air Curaçao seems to be covered with giant mushrooms, really fuel tanks. There is more oil than water. Oil tankers bring in water for washing, and people say that they know when a person has taken a bath because he smells of kerosene.

The San Blas Islands

IT is hard to say where the West Indies end. After the ABC Islands, a lacy collar of small islands extends past Venezuela and Colombia to Panama, where there are about four hundred little San Blas Islands whose official name is Archipiélago de las Mulatas (tawny or brownish). The San Blas Indians who live on them have changed less since the days of Columbus than other people anywhere in the West Indies, and from them possibly we can get an idea of what life was like on the Antillean chain before the Spaniards came to the New World.

The San Blas Indians are small people. A man dresses in a shirt and pair of trousers. A girl or woman wears a short-sleeved blouse gaily decorated, a long skirt, a head scarf, a gold nose ring, and ornamental chains wound round the lower legs. Everybody goes barefoot. The men fish from mahogany dugouts, called *cayucos*, which are quite primitive.

87

The men must sail to the mainland to farm, for only the coconut tree grows in the sandy soil. Also there is no water, so the people drink coconut milk. They eat coconut meat, make chairs and fishing equipment from the trunks of the trees, also clothing and hats, the hammocks they sleep in, roofs for their houses, ropes, and brooms to sweep their dirt floors. They use the shells of the coconut for dishes, the husks and broken shells for fuel, and burn coconut oil in their tiny lamps. Their houses are of the bohio type with a thick palm thatch that keeps out tropical downpours. The walls are made of slender bamboo poles, fastened together upright like our solid garden fences.

The woman is really the head of the family. When a man is first married, he goes to live with his father-in-law and has to work for him, too, until a daughter is born. Then he can set up his own household. Also, women are the businessmen. When the supply boat comes, they load the family cayucos with coconuts, row out to the boat, bargain to sell their coconuts, and buy from the boat the few supplies they need.

The San Blas Indians have mahogany-colored skin, but occasionally boys and girls are born with pure white skin and light hair. Albino children alone may go outside the house when there is an eclipse of the moon. With their bows and arrows they must defend their people from the horrible dragon or big black dog that takes bites out of the moon. Albinos are known as "moon children."

The San Blas Indians have many strange ways but none stranger than the marriage custom. In warm countries children grow up fast. At the age of fourteen most San Blas girls are ready to be married. The girl tells her parents what boy she wants to marry. They place her in a strong hammock, while the young married men of the village carry the bridegroom bodily from his home and put him in the hammock with the bride. Three times he jumps out and runs away and each time he is caught and brought back. If he does not stay after being caught the third time, it is a sign that the young lady must pick someone else.